mazing Saints & their Awesome Animals

COLORING BOOK

Saint Francis & the Wolf

Saint Anthony & the Donkey

Saint Bridget & the Fox

Saint Benedict & the Raven

Saint Jerome & the Lion

Saint Modomnoc & the Bees

Saint Hugh & the Swan

Blessed Maria Bagnesi & her Cats

Saint Verdiana & the Snakes

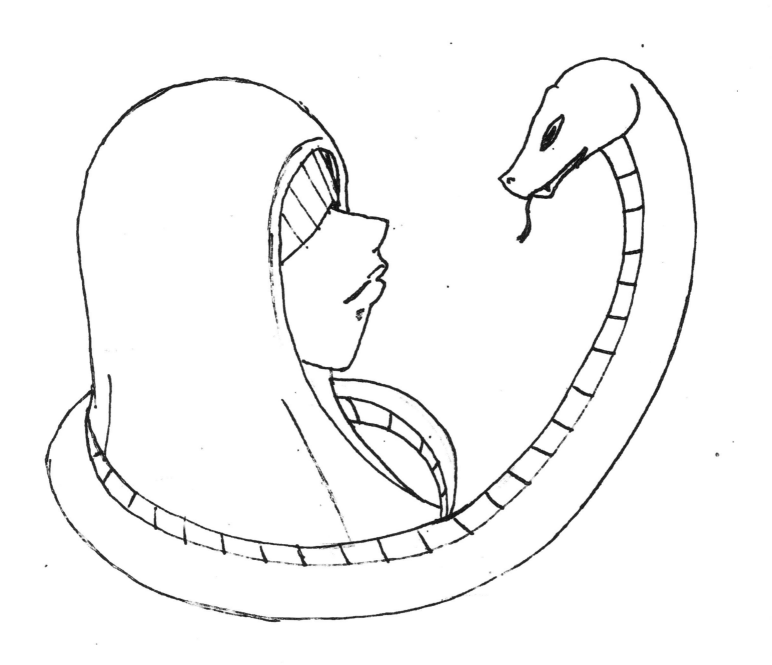

Other children's books available from
CaritasPress.org and CatholicWord.com

ARCHANGELA'S HORSE
Archangela comes to understand God's will when her beloved and loyal horse refuses to take her where she wants to go.
By Sherry Boas

SAINT JOHN BOSCO AND HIS BIG GRAY DOG
Colorfully-illustrated story of a very special canine guardian who appeared out of nowhere to protect St. John Bosco whenever he was in danger. By Hayley Madieros

ENCYCLOPEDIA OF PEG SAINTS
Get to know 36 saints in an engaging and easy to "absorb" format, centered around colorful hand-painted peg dolls collected and cherished by Catholic kids everywhere. By Maggie & Michael Jetty

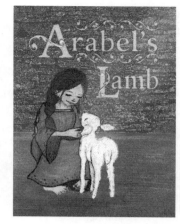

ARABEL'S LAMB
A young girl's compassion is tested to the limits in this gripping tale about love and sacrifice. Loosely based on the legend of St. George and the Dragon. By Sherry Boas

LITTLE MAXIMUS MYERS
Little Maximus Myers never liked being little, until one day, while carrying the cross in the procession at Mass, he discovered how our weaknesses can bring us closer to Christ. By Sherry Boas

MIRACULOUS ME
A mother and father dream of the future as they celebrate the precious gift of life, the baby who is about to arrive. What will the days of her life hold? By Ruth Pendergast Sissel & Tina Tolliver Matney

BARNYARD BLISS
All of creation rejoices as word of the baby owlet spreads throughout the farm from one animal to the next. By Ruth Pendergast Sissel & Tina Tolliver Matney

VICTORIA'S SPARROWS
A young girl sees God's providence at work after her day takes a turn she didn't expect. By Sherry Boas

BILLOWTAIL
Little creatures on a big adventure in medieval Spain! 220-page Novel. By Sherry Boas

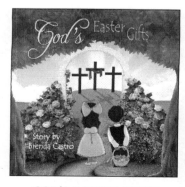

GOD'S EASTER GIFTS
A very special Easter egg hunt shows brother and sister, Pablo and Bella, that there's much more to Easter than candy and toys. By Brenda Castro

THE GIFT IN THE MANGER
When their feeding trough ends up serving as a bed for a tiny baby, the animals get a glimpse into God's loving plan to save the world. Like every one of us, each of the animals gathered around the manger has a struggle to overcome. They, like us, find the answer in Jesus, the only one who can fix our brokenness, heal our imperfections and give us the gift that makes us whole – the gift of Himself. By Sherry Boas

That wondrous night seen through the eyes of the animals. Baby Jesus' future is foretold, and we see the much needed grace He brings to our lives.

Books for Mom & Dad

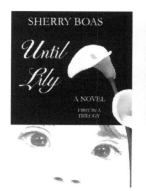

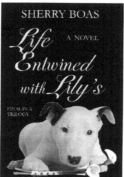

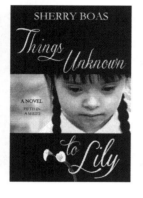

THE LILY SERIES BY SHERRY BOAS
Until Lily
Wherever Lily Goes
Life Entwined with Lily's
The Things Lily Knew
Things Unknown to Lily
A Little Like Lily

"...You will be entranced, you will experience the joys and sorrows of the characters, you will cry, and you will not be able to put Lily down."
– Dr. Jeff Mirus of CatholicCulture.org

The transforming power of love is at the heart of Sherry Boas' poignant series about the people whose lives are moved by a woman with Down syndrome. Lily's story is told with such brutal yet touching honesty, it will have you laughing one minute and reduced to tears the next.

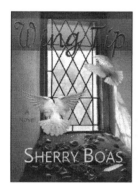

WING TIP
A Novel

Dante De Luz's steel was forged in his youth, in the crucible of harsh losses and triumphant love. But that steel gets tested like never before as his mother's deathbed confession reveals something startling about his father and presents the young Catholic priest with the toughest challenge of his life, with stakes that couldn't get any higher.

"Aside from death and taxes, here's one more thing that is certain in this life: Sherry Boas' *Wing Tip*, will be a classic of Catholic literature. Magnificent read, highly recommended."

Robert Curtis,
The Catholic Sun

Rosary meditations for everyone in the family

Dads   Moms   Children   Teens   Grandparents   Altar Servers   Special full-color **Gift Edition and Journal for Mom**

CaritasPress.org

Amazing Saints & their Awesome Animals Coloring Book
Copyright © 2016 Maria Boas (artwork)
Printed in the USA

First Edition
10 9 8 7 6 5 4 3 2 1
ISBN: 978-1-940209-28-9

Contact Sherry@LilyTrilogy.com

CARITAS PRESS

CaritasPress.org

Caritas Press was founded in 2011 with the mission of shedding light on things eternal in a culture that is becoming increasingly blind to the wonders of God's works and numb to His boundless love. Making use of the subtle and the beautiful, Caritas Press hopes to play a part in igniting in children and adults a desire to know God more fully. For a full listing of all Caritas titles for children, youths and adults, visit CaritasPress.org.

Made in the USA
Middletown, DE
24 June 2016